NATIONAL GEOGRAPHIC KiDS

ANIMALS
Quiz
Book

Published by Collins
An imprint of HarperCollins Publishers
Westerhill Road
Bishopbriggs
Glasgow G64 2QT
www.harpercollins.co.uk

HarperCollins Publishers
Macken House, 39/40 Mayor Street Upper, Dublin 1, D01 C9W8, Ireland

In association with National Geographic Partners, LLC

NATIONAL GEOGRAPHIC and the Yellow Border Design are trademarks
of the National Geographic Society and used under license.

First published 2021

ISBN 978-0-00-840934-0

10 9 8 7 6 5 4 3

A catalogue record for this book is available from the British Library.

Printed in India

If you would like to comment on any aspect of this book, please contact us
at the above address or online.
natgeokidsbooks.co.uk
collins.reference@harpercollins.co.uk

Paper from responsible sources.

Acknowledgements
Text by Richard Happer

Images
P10: bowhead whale image © NPS Photo/Alamy Stock Photo
P57: Goliath frog image © imageBROKER/Alamy Stock Photo
All other images © Shutterstock.com

MIX
Paper | Supporting
responsible forestry
FSC™ C007454

NATIONAL GEOGRAPHIC KiDS

ANIMALS Quiz Book

300 brain busting trivia questions

Contents

HOW MUCH DO YOU KNOW ABOUT YOUR PETS?

DID YOU KNOW?

The canine sense of smell is very sensitive, and some dogs can be trained to detect certain diseases by smell, such as some cancers, diabetes and malaria.

1 **Cats spend most of their time sleeping.** True or false?

2 **Goldfish have a memory span of how long?**
a. 3 months   b. 3 hours   c. 3 seconds

3 **Where are budgerigars originally from in the wild?**
a. The Amazon Rainforest   b. Australia   c. Alaska

4 **Hamsters are 'crepuscular' – what does this mean?**
a. They like to creep about.
b. Their eyes glow in the dark.
c. They are most active at dawn and dusk.

5 **How many baby rabbit descendants could one pair of rabbits create in 4 years?**
a. 3.7 million   b. 10,000   c. 250

6 **Golden retrievers are a popular breed of pet dog. Where were they first bred?**
a. Paris, France   b. Golder's Green, London   c. The Scottish Highlands

7 **Guinea pigs are actually...**
a. Rodents from Guinea in West Africa
b. Miniature pigs from Papua New Guinea
c. Rodents from the Andes mountains in South America

8 **What makes the Basenji hound special?**
a. It is vegetarian.   b. It cannot bark.   c. It never chases cats.

9 **The world's largest dog show is called...**
a. Wimbledon   b. Crufts   c. The Barking Mad Show

10 **What is unusual about the Manx breed of cat?**
a. It loves swimming.   b. It is afraid of mice.   c. It has a very short tail.

HOW MUCH DO YOU KNOW ABOUT YOUR PETS?

DID YOU KNOW?

A rabbit's teeth never stop growing. Nibbling on grass and hay keep their chompers from getting too long.

1 **True.** Cats spend around 13–16 hours a day sleeping, which is about 70% of their lives.

2 **a.** 3 months. Goldfish aren't as forgetful as people think. They can understand different colours, shapes and sounds, as well as recognise their owners.

3 **b.** Australia.

4 **c.** Crepuscular means that hamsters are most active at dawn and dusk.

5 **a.** 3.7 million. A female rabbit can start to have babies when she is only 3 months old and can have a litter every month. So if all her children have children and then they have children...

6 **c.** Golden retrievers were first bred in the Scottish Highlands. An aristocrat, who lived in Glen Affric, loved hunting and bred the dogs to help.

7 **c.** Guinea pigs are actually rodents from the Andes mountains in South America. It's unclear where their name came from.

8 **b.** Basenji hounds don't bark but they do make a sort of chortling sound.

9 **b.** Crufts is the biggest dog show in the world. It was first held in 1891.

10 **c.** Manx cats don't have long tails like most other cats – they just have a very short and stumpy tail. Their short tails are a result of a genetic mutation that spread through the population.

DOLPHINS AND WHALES

1

What is the name for the tail fin of dolphins and whales?

a. Wiggle fin

b. Fluke

c. Dorsal fin

2

What family of animals do dolphins and whales belong to?

a. Rodents

b. Equines

c. Cetaceans

3

Whales dive the deepest of all air-breathing creatures. What type of whale has been recorded to have the deepest dive?

a. Cuvier's beaked whales

b. Beluga whales

c. Humpback whales

4

One of the smallest species of whale is a beluga whale. What colour is it?

a. White

b. Grey

c. Blue-black

5

What is unusual about the bowhead whale?

a. It eats sharks.

b. It has the largest mouth of any animal.

c. It can do a double somersault out of the water.

DID YOU KNOW?

Beluga whales are nicknamed 'sea canaries' because of the huge variety of sounds they produce.

6

How do bottlenose dolphins sleep?
a. With one eye open
b. Upside down
c. On the sea bed

7

Where does this unusual-looking pink dolphin live?
a. The English Channel
b. Antarctica
c. The Amazon river

8

A baby blue whale is about the size of a fridge when it is born. True or false?

9

Whales and dolphins use a wide range of clicks, whistles and other sounds. Why do they do this?
a. To talk to their friends and family members.
b. To locate prey.
c. To attract a mate.

10

Why do scientists think dolphins surf waves?
a. To catch small fish that swim close to the shore.
b. It's a good way to hide from sharks.
c. For fun.

11

DOLPHINS AND WHALES

DID YOU KNOW?

Dolphins usually swim around in a leisurely fashion, but they can reach speeds of around 20 km/h.

1
b. Fluke.
Dolphins and whales move their fluke up and down to thrust themselves through the water.

2
c. Cetaceans.
There are 89 species of aquatic mammals in this family, including whales, dolphins, porpoises. The word is pronounced 'set-aish-ans'.

3
a.
Scientists attached tracking tags to Cuvier's beaked whales and discovered that one of them dived to nearly 3000 m. This is about as deep as stacking 3 Scafell Pikes (England's highest mountain) on top of each other!

4
a. White.
Beluga whale calves are actually born grey or brown, but fade to white when they are around 5 years old.

5
b. It has the largest mouth of any animal.
The bowhead whale's mouth is big enough to swallow a minibus—but it only eats tiny sea creatures.

6
a. With one eye open.
Dolphins' breathing is not automatic so if they fell into a deep unconscious sleep, they would stop breathing and drown. To avoid this, they only let one half of their brains sleep at a time, while the other half stays alert, which means one eye is always open, even when they're asleep.

7
c. The Amazon River.
There are 5 species of dolphins that live in rivers —this is the Amazon River dolphin that lives in the Amazon River.

8
False.
At up to 8 m long and weighing in at 3 tonnes, a blue whale is the biggest baby in the world. It is much bigger than a fridge—it is more like the size of a van!

9
a, b and c!
Whales and dolphins chatter to communicate with other members of their pod. They use echolocation when hunting to find prey, and they also show off to potential mates.

10
c. For fun.
It seems like dolphins simply love catching waves!

REPTILES

1

Reptiles are...
a. Warm-blooded
b. Cold-blooded
c. Don't have blood

2

Snakes swallow their food whole and can eat prey that is bigger than the diameter of their own head.
True or false?

3

There are no venomous snakes native to the UK.
True or false?

4

The basilisk lizard shares its name with a legendary monster that could kill with a single glance. Why else is this real-world creature famous?
a. It can fly.
b. It breathes fire.
c. It can run on water.

5

Crocodiles produce so much stomach acid that they can digest bones.
True or false?

6

What makes viviparous lizards different from most lizards?

a. They live in large social groups.

b. They sing to each other.

c. They give birth to live young.

7

Chameleons are known for being able to change colour to blend in with their surroundings. What else can they do?

a. Move their eyes independently of each other.

b. Climb trees using their prehensile tails.

c. Shoot out their tongues to catch prey.

8

Hawksbill turtles lay the most eggs at one time of any reptile. What is the most eggs that scientists have recorded in one clutch?

a. 42

b. 242

c. 1242

9

What is the largest lizard species?

a. Komodo dragon

b. Panther chameleon

c. Spiny iguana

10

Match these snakes to their claim to fame.

a. Black mamba   i. Longest

b. Inland taipan   ii. Most venomous

c. Reticulated python   iii. Fastest

REPTILES

1

b. Cold-blooded.
Reptiles are cold-blooded, so the temperature of their body depends on how warm their surroundings are.

2

True.
Snakes have flexible, loosely connected jaws which move separately to stretch over the prey.

3

False.
The adder, or common viper, is venomous. Its bite is rarely fatal in humans but can make people very ill and require medical attention.

4

c. It can run on water.
The basilisk sprints across the surface of water using only its back feet. Its back feet have large flaps of skin between the toes which, when it runs quickly across water, help it to create tiny air pockets that stop it from sinking.

5

True.
Crocodiles can produce stomach acid 10 times faster than any other animal!

DID YOU KNOW?

Certain types of lizards, like geckos, can shed their tail if a predator grabs it, meaning the lizard can make a quick escape if it needs to.

6

c. They give birth to live young.
Viviparous lizards give birth to live young, but most reptiles lay eggs.

7

a, b and c.
Chameleons have a lot of amazing skills – their feet also work like pincers so that they can grip and balance on branches.

8

b. 242.
Hawksbill turtles lay the most eggs in a single clutch. But green turtles can lay around 500 eggs in one season – that's around 100–200 eggs over 3–5 clutches.

9

a. Komodo dragon.
Komodo dragons can grow up to 3 m long and weigh 100 kg which is almost twice the size and weight of a fridge-freezer!

10

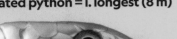

a. Black mamba = iii. fastest (20 km/h)
b. Inland taipan = ii. most venomous
c. Reticulated python = i. longest (8 m)

MAMMALS

DID YOU KNOW?

Elephants' tusks are actually teeth! They're very large incisor teeth, which start growing when elephants are around one year old.

1

Sharks are mammals.

2

Humans are the only real bipedal (meaning to move on only two legs) mammals.

3

Mammals are the only creatures with hair or fur.

4

Mammals feed their young on eggs.

5

Bats are flying mammals, and a flying fox is actually a bat.

6

Elephants are the tallest land mammals.

7

Sea otters have the densest fur of any mammal.

8

There are more species of rodent than any other type of mammal.

9

Pigs, rhinoceroses, moose and camels are all hoofed mammals.

10

Mammals are cold-blooded.

TRUE or FALSE

DID YOU KNOW?

When marmots dig their burrow, they use both their front and back feet. The front feet scrape the soil out, and the back feet then push it away from the hole.

1
FALSE.
Sharks are actually fish, however, sea creatures like porpoises, whales and dolphins are mammals who breathe air and give birth to live young.

2
TRUE.
Some other mammals such as kangaroos move on two legs, but not all the time.

3
TRUE.
Hair helps mammals keep warm by trapping air next to the skin.

4
FALSE.
Mammals feed their young on milk.

5
TRUE.
Bats are flying mammals and flying foxes are one of the largest species, weighing up to 1.45 kg.

6
FALSE.
Giraffes are the tallest, reaching 5.5 m. Elephants are the heaviest land mammals.

7
TRUE.
Sea otters' fur is so warm that they can spend almost all their time in the ocean.

8
TRUE.
Around 40% of all the world's mammal species are rodents, including mice, rats, squirrels, rabbits, beavers and porcupines.

9
TRUE.
Hoofed mammals are known as ungulates and also include horses, deer and hippos.

10
FALSE.
Mammals are, in fact, warm-blooded, which means that they can keep their internal body temperature constant regardless of their environment.

ANIMAL COMMUNICATION

 1

Bees that have found nectar do what to tell other bees about it?

a. A waggle dance

b. Fly around in a circle

c. A wiggle call

 2

How do male gorillas show their strength?

a. Pull trees down

b. Throw bananas at other males

c. Beat their chests with their hands

 3

Which type of owls are famous for their 'tu-whit tu-whoo' calls?

a. Hooty owls   b. Barn owls   c. Tawny owls

4

Grasshoppers are one of many creatures that communicate by stridulation. What is stridulation?

a. Rapid singing

b. Rubbing body parts together

c. Head-butting trees

 5

How does this snake scare away predators?

a. It shakes a rattle in its tail.

b. It spits venom.

c. It moves its head from side to side.

Do lions and tigers purr like house cats do?
a. Yes, they purr quite often.
b. They can purr but hardly ever do.
c. No, they cannot purr.

DID YOU KNOW?

White rhinos communicate via their dung! Their poo contains different-smelling chemicals that let other rhinos know if, for example, another rhino is ill.

How many different alarm calls do vervet monkeys have?
a. 2   b. 3   c. 4

Which bird can sing hundreds of different songs?
a. Nightingale   b. Starling   c. Sea eagle

What do rabbits do to tell other rabbits about danger?
a. Scratch earth up into the air
b. Hop up and down on the spot
c. Thump their rear feet on the ground

Ants leave a trail of special chemicals on the ground that can be followed by other ants. True or false?

ANIMAL COMMUNICATION

1   **a.** The waggle dance is a figure-of-eight that tells other bees the direction and distance of flowers.

2   **c.** Gorillas beat their chests when they sense danger and also to show off to females.

3   **c.** Many owl species hoot, but it is two tawny owls calling to each other that make the famous 'tu-whit tu-whoo'. The female calls out with the 'tu-whit' sound and the male answers with 'tu-whoo'! These return calls from the male tawny owl reveal all sorts of information to the female about its territory and size.

4   **b.** Grasshoppers stridulate by rubbing a scraper on their hind leg against their wing.

5   **a.** The rattlesnake makes a rattling noise by rapidly moving segments of scales in its tail. A segment is left behind each time it sheds its skin.

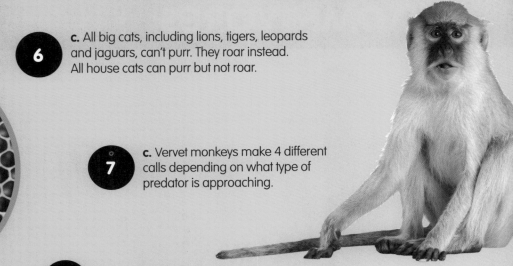

6 **c.** All big cats, including lions, tigers, leopards and jaguars, can't purr. They roar instead. All house cats can purr but not roar.

7 **c.** Vervet monkeys make 4 different calls depending on what type of predator is approaching.

8 **a.** The quality of a male nightingale's song helps the female decide if he will be a suitable mate.

9 **c.** Rabbits usually thump with one foot, but sometimes use both rear feet.

10 **True.** Ants use special chemicals called pheromones to alert other ants to things like danger, or to lead them to sources of food.

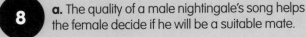

25

CARNIVORES, HERBIVORES AND OMNIVORES

DID YOU KNOW?

A group of zebra can be called 'a dazzle'!

1 What does a carnivore eat?
a. Only plants   b. Only meat   c. A mix of meat and plants

2 Bactrian camels are herbivores, and they can store fat in their humps that can be converted to water and energy when needed. How many humps does a Bactrian camel have?
a. 2   b. 1   c. None

3 Giant pandas are almost completely herbivorous. What plant do they eat for 99% of their meals?
a. Eucalyptus   b. Bamboo   c. Privet hedges

4 What is the largest land carnivore in the UK?
a. Red deer   b. Cat   c. Badger

5 Despite being an omnivore, which weasel with a ravenous appetite for meat will happily try to steal kills from bears and wolves?
a. Raccoon   b. Otter   c. Wolverine

6 Red foxes are omnivores and will eat a whole host of things, depending on their habitat. Is a 'vixen' a male fox or a female fox?

7 Zebras are herbivores and spend most of their time grazing the grasslands of Africa. Are they black with white stripes or white with black stripes?

8 Grizzly bears are true omnivores, munching almost any food they can get their paws on, including meat, fish, birds, carrion, nuts and grasses. But how fast can they run in pursuit of a meal?
a. 36 km/h   b. 46 km/h   c. 56 km/h

9 Great white sharks are carnivores and are the largest predatory fish in the world. On average, how many teeth do they have?
a. 100   b. 300   c. 500

10 What is the largest herbivore in the world?
a. White rhino   b. Moose   c. African elephant

CARNIVORES, HERBIVORES AND OMNIVORES

1 **b.** Carnivores only eat meat. Herbivores only eat plants, and omnivores eat a mixture of food, including meat and plants.

2 **a.** Bactrian camels have two humps; a camel with one hump is known as a dromedary.

3 **b.** Giant pandas survive on a diet made up of mainly bamboo, but some pandas in zoos are given fruit, vegetables and special biscuits to top up their diet.

4 **c.** The largest land carnivore in the UK is the badger, but the largest UK carnivore overall is the grey seal.

5 **c.** Wolverines are fiercely strong predators with a taste for meat.

6 A vixen is a female fox. The male is known as a dog, tod or reynard.

7 Zebras are black with white stripes.

8 **c.** Grizzly bears can run at 56 km/h to catch prey like deer and moose.

9 **b.** Great white sharks have around 300 teeth, which are triangular and serrated. About 50 of these teeth sit in their main jaws, followed behind by multiple rows of developing teeth.

10 **c.** The largest herbivore in the world is the African elephant, whose diet consists of roots, grasses, fruit and bark.

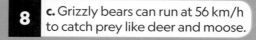

PARASITES AND SYMBIOTES

1

Parasitism is a harmful relationship between two animals. True or false?

2

The cuckoo is a well-known wild bird—in what way is it a parasite?

a. It steals the eggs of eagles and eats them.

b. It lays its eggs in other birds' nests.

c. It perches on the backs of cows and eats their hair.

3

Humans get parasites too, such as head lice. What do head lice feed on?

a. Hair

b. Dandruff

c. Blood

4

Bees visit flowers to get nectar, which they use to make honey. But what do flowers get from the deal?

a. The bees also eat the aphids that eat flower petals.

b. Bees spread pollen from flower to flower, helping the plants to reproduce.

c. Bees' buzzing helps flowers grow faster.

5

Malaria is a deadly disease spread by what parasite?

a. Fleas

b. Mosquitoes

c. Tapeworms

6

How does the clownfish keep itself safe?

a. It makes friends with a shark for protection.

b. It hides in an old turtle shell and only comes out at night.

c. It is covered in a thick layer of mucus which it uses to protect itself so it can hide in sea anemones which are poisonous to other creatures.

7

What do big fish do when they see a Bluestreak cleaner wrasse fish?

a. They hide.

b. Line up to let the wrasse eat sea lice from their scales.

c. Eat the wrasse.

8

How do kangaroos get rid of lice and other parasites from their skin?

a. They go swimming in warm water.

b. They shed their fur.

c. They groom themselves with specially evolved claws.

9

Farmers sometimes use parasitic wasps as a natural way of killing pests. How many species of parasitic wasps are there?

a. 100

b. 1000

c. More than 100,000

10

What parasitic mammals have evolved to feed on the blood of other animals?

a. Vampire bats

b. Vampire rats

c. Vampire cats

PARASITES AND SYMBIOTES

1

True.
Parasitism is when one animal lives with or inside a host animal, and the host animal gets hurt. For example, barnacles are parasites for swimming crabs—the barnacles can root themselves inside a crab and hurt them.

2

b.
Cuckoos lay their eggs in other birds' nests. When the young cuckoos hatch, they are fed by birds that aren't their parents.

3

c.
Head lice feed on blood... Nasty!

4

b.
Bees help with pollination —if it weren't for bees and other insects, farmers would have no crops.

5

b.
Mosquitoes spread malaria.

6

c.

The clownfish benefits the anemone by providing it with nutrients and by attracting prey for the sea anemone to eat.

7

b.

Bigger fish line up for little wrasses to eat their parasites at 'cleaning stations,' like cars at a car wash!

8

c.

Lots of animals, including kangaroos, groom themselves or each other to remove parasites.

9

c.

Parasitic wasps lay their eggs in another insect, such as a caterpillar. The eggs hatch into larvae that eat the caterpillar.

10

a.

There are three species of vampire bats and they all drink blood.

IN YOUR GARDEN

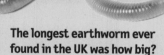

1 The longest earthworm ever found in the UK was how big?

a. 30 cm long

b. 40 cm long

c. 50 cm long

2 Moles live underground and eat worms and other invertebrates. What ability is the star-nosed mole famous for?

a. It is the fastest-digging mammal in the world.

b. It is the slowest-breathing mammal in the world.

c. It is the fastest-eating mammal in the world.

3 The silk that spiders use to build their webs is stronger than steel. True or false?

4 What is the name of this butterfly?

a. Red admiral

b. Painted lady

c. Scarlet bandit

5 Blue tits and great tits feed their young on caterpillars. How many caterpillars do they deliver to their family each year?

a. 1000

b. 5000

c. 10,000

6

There are now thousands of urban foxes living in every UK city—why?

a. Foxes can adapt well to the urban lifestyle.

b. Farmers chased them away from the countryside.

c. Pet foxes escaped and bred.

7

Which of these statements about hedgehogs is true?

a. They got their name from the snuffling noise they make while hunting for food in hedgerows.

b. One hedgehog could be home to around 100 fleas.

c. They can travel up to 3 km a night looking for food.

8

Ladybirds are pretty and also useful, as they eat pests such as aphids. How many aphids do you think a single ladybird can eat in a year?

a. 1000   b. 5000   c. 10,000

9

Squirrels can help forests grow. How do they do this?

a. By forgetting where they buried their nuts

b. By scraping mould off trees

c. By scaring away deer that might eat saplings

10

How do barn owls track their prey?

a. Their sharp eyesight

b. Their excellent sense of smell

c. Their keen sense of hearing

IN YOUR GARDEN

1

b. The worm was found in a vegetable garden in Widnes and was given the name 'Dave'.

3

True. Spider silk is very light but incredibly strong—it is five times as strong as steel.

2

c. Star-nosed moles can detect, identify and eat prey in as little as 120 milliseconds—that's too fast for human eyes to see.

4

a. The red admiral is a bright butterfly that is one of the last to be seen before winter sets in.

5

c. Blue tits and great tits fly tens of kilometres a day to gather food for their young.

b. Ladybirds can eat 5000 aphids a year, which is why farmers love them.

8

6

a. Leafy suburbs with gardens and hedges are a wonderful place for foxes. There are sheds to hide under and plenty of food including mice, birds, fruit and human rubbish!

9

a. Squirrels bury lots of nuts to save them for later. But they only ever go back to around 30% of the nuts they bury – some of the others grow into trees.

7

a, b and c. Hedgehogs are famous for their bodies covered in prickly spines. They look cute, but be careful not to touch if you're lucky enough to spot one in your garden!

10

c. Barn owls can successfully catch their prey even in pitch darkness.

WHO AM I?

Match each animal photo to its correct name.

Jerboa

Patagonian mara

Naked mole-rat

Babirusa

Maned wolf

Gerenuk

Axolotl

Fossa

Sunda flying lemur

Dugong

WHO AM I?

Axolotl

The axolotl is also known as the Mexican walking fish. It is a type of salamander.

Maned wolf

The maned wolf has the colouring of a fox, but it is neither a fox nor a wolf. It is a unique species of the dog family from South America.

Patagonian mara

The Patagonian mara is a large rabbit-like rodent from Argentina.

Naked mole-rat

The naked mole-rat is the longest-living rodent, living up to 32 years.

Gerenuk

The gerenuk is an antelope that is sometimes called the giraffe gazelle. It lives in Africa.

The dugong, also known as the sea cow, is a large aquatic mammal that eats mostly sea grass.

Dugong

The babirusa is also known as the deer-pig and it lives in Indonesia.

Babirusa

The fossa is a cat-like mammal from Madagascar.

Fossa

The Sunda flying lemur is not a lemur and doesn't fly. It is also known as a 'colugo' that glides as it leaps among trees.

Sunda flying lemur

Jerboas are nocturnal rodents that hop around desert areas of the Arabian Peninsula, eastern Europe, northern Africa and Asia.

Jerboa

EXTINCT BUT STILL AMAZING

1 Which dinosaur had the longest teeth, with gnashers up to 15 cm long?
a. Megalosaurus   b. Tyrannosaurus rex   c. Iguanodon

2 Dinosaurs lived during three 'periods' of geological time – can you put them in the right order from oldest to most recent?
a. Jurassic period
b. Cretaceous period
c. Triassic period

3 At 12 m long, a deinosuchus was big enough to hunt large dinosaurs, but what type of creature was it?
a. Giant turtle   b. Giant mouse   c. Giant crocodile

4 How big was the wingspan of the pterosaur quetzalcoatlus?
a. Up to 10.5 m   b. Up to 8.5 m   c. Up to 5.5 m

5 We now think that the after-effects of an asteroid hitting Earth wiped out the dinosaurs 65 million years ago. Near what modern location did it hit Earth?
a. The Maldives   b. Mexico   c. Manchester

DID YOU KNOW?
Woolly mammoths had a thick layer — around 10 cm — of fat under their skin to stop them from freezing to death.

6 Which two reasons below caused woolly mammoths to go extinct?
a. Climate change
b. Attacks by sabre-toothed tigers
c. Human hunting

7 Paraceratherium was the largest land mammal that ever lived, weighing up to 20 tonnes and measuring 5.5 m tall and 8 m long. What modern creature is it related to?
a. Elephant   b. Rhinoceros   c. Giraffe

8 From which extinct animal is this part of a skeleton?
a. Sabre-toothed cat
b. Spear-toothed dog
c. Great carnivorous squirrel

9 Trilobites looked like woodlice, ranging from 1–70 cm. How long did they exist?
a. 100 million years   b. 200 million years   c. 300 million years

10 A huge coprolite measuring 44 cm long came from a Tyrannosaurus rex. What is a coprolite?
a. A fossilised heart   b. A fossilised brain   c. Fossilised dung

43

EXTINCT BUT STILL AMAZING

1 **b.** A Tyrannosaurus rex's teeth measured up to 15 cm, and were curved with a serrated edge to help them slash skin and crunch bone.

2 **c, a, b.** The Triassic period is the oldest, ranging from 252–201 million years ago, followed by the Jurassic period from 201–145 million years ago, finishing with the Cretaceous period, which lasted 79 million years from 145–66 million years ago.

3 **c.** A deinosuchus would have looked very similar to today's crocodiles – only twice as long!

4 **a.** Quetzalcoatlus was the biggest flying creature that ever existed. It was similar in size to a small single-seat plane!

5 **b.** The asteroid that initiated the extinction of the dinosaurs hit modern-day Mexico.

6 **a. and c.** Woolly mammoths disappeared 4000 years ago as a result of a change in climate and humans hunting them.

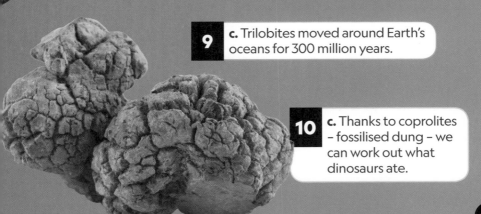

7 **b.** Paraceratherium was a member of the rhinoceros family, but it didn't have a horn.

8 **a.** Sabre-toothed cats roamed the planet up until about 11,000 years ago, so our human ancestors would have had to worry about their attacks.

9 **c.** Trilobites moved around Earth's oceans for 300 million years.

10 **c.** Thanks to coprolites – fossilised dung – we can work out what dinosaurs ate.

ANIMAL EXTREMES

1
What is the fastest animal in the world?
a. Cheetah
b. Kangaroo
c. Peregrine falcon

2
Which animal makes the loudest noise?
a. A tiger roaring
b. A fin whale singing
c. A baboon shrieking

3
Which of these animals has the most teeth?
a. Saltwater crocodile
b. Snail
c. Great white shark

4
A box jellyfish has enough venom to kill up to 5 humans.

True or false?

5
What is the longest animal in the world?
a. Giant squid
b. Boot-lace worm
c. Portuguese man o'war

6
Which creature has the largest brain relative to its size?
a. Ant
b. Human
c. Elephant

7

Which animal has the most bite force?

a. Crocodile

b. Grizzly bear

c. Hippopotamus

8

What is the heaviest animal that ever lived?

a. Elephant

b. Blue whale

c. Diplodocus

9

Which of these animals eats the most food, relative to its size?

a. Blue whale

b. Pygmy shrew

c. Panda

10

Which animal sleeps for the most hours per day?

a. Cat

b. Sloth

c. Koala

ANIMAL EXTREMES

1

c.

The peregrine falcon is the world speed champ. It has been measured stooping (diving from above to catch its prey) at 389 km/h. The cheetah is the fastest land animal with a top speed of 96 km/h.

2

b.

A fin whale's song has been recorded at 188 decibels. To put this into context, a fire engine siren is around 120 decibels, meaning a fin whale's song is much louder!

3

b.

Snail! Incredibly, snails have between 2000 and 15,000 tiny teeth. Great white sharks have around 300 teeth (50 in their main jaws plus 5 rows of developing teeth) and saltwater crocodiles have around 66.

4

False.

A single box jellyfish can actually have enough venom to kill more than 50 humans.

5

b.

Boot-lace worm. This ribbon worm lives in the North Sea. One specimen that washed up in 1864 was more than 55 m long.

6

a.

An ant's brain accounts for around 14% of its body weight. A human brain is about 2.5% of body weight, and an elephant's is just 0.1%.

7

a.

A saltwater crocodile has been measured to have a bite force of 16,414 newtons. That's around twice as strong a bite as a hippo.

8

b.

The blue whale is the largest animal known to have ever existed. It can reach over 30 m in length and weigh 190 tonnes. The largest dinosaur was Argentinosaurus, which may have weighed 100 tonnes.

9

b.

The American pygmy shrew. It only weighs around 4 grams, but its metabolism is so fast that it must eat three times its own bodyweight every day. If it went a single hour without eating, it would die.

10

c.

The koala sleeps up to 22 hours a day.

MARSUPIALS

1
Marsupials are not mammals.

2
Marsupial animals only live in Australia.

3
Marsupials carry their young around on their backs for the first months of their life.

DID YOU KNOW?
Marsupials are usually tiny when they're born. A newborn kangaroo joey weighs just 1 gram!

4
The largest marsupial is Australia's red kangaroo.

5
The pouch on a wombat opens backwards.

6
Marsupial lions once roamed Australia.

7
There was once a marsupial – a giant wombat – the size of a rhinoceros.

8
A marsupial baby is called a joey.

9
New Zealand has no native marsupials.

10
The name koala means 'no drink'.

MARSUPIALS

1

FALSE.
Marsupials are mammals because they produce milk for their young, are warm-blooded and have hair or fur.

2

FALSE.
There are marsupial animals in Indonesia and many species of opossum in the Americas.

3

FALSE.
Marsupials carry their young around in a pouch on their belly.

4

TRUE.
The largest-ever kangaroo stood around 2 m tall and weighed 230 kg.

5

TRUE.
Wombats dig burrows with their powerful claws. Their backward-facing pouch stops soil from flicking over their young.

6

TRUE.
The marsupial lion was about the size of a jaguar and had the strongest bite of any mammal ever. It went extinct around 40,000 years ago.

7

TRUE.
These creatures the size of a rhinoceros were called diprotodon. They were 3 m long and weighed around 2790 kg. They went extinct around the same time as the marsupial lion.

8

TRUE.
Marsupial babies are called joeys.

9

TRUE.
Marsupials never made it as far as New Zealand, despite it being Australia's neighbour.

10

TRUE.
The local Aboriginal people gave koalas the name because they get all the moisture they need from eucalyptus leaves and hardly ever drink.

AMPHIBIANS

1

The name 'amphibian' literally means:
a. Water-loving
b. Animal that changes
c. Both kinds of life

2

Nearly all amphibians are carnivorous.
True or false?

3

What is the largest species of amphibian?
a. Chinese salamander
b. Japanese meganewt
c. Korean horned toad

4

Frogs have smooth shiny skin, but toads have rough and dry skin.
True or false?

5

How does the Spanish ribbed newt defend itself?
a. It spits venom.
b. It stands on its hind legs / jumps in the air.
c. It turns its ribs into poisonous spikes.

DID YOU KNOW?

Amphibians have glands on their skin which produce substances that help protect them from injury and speed up healing.

6

The axolotl, or Mexican walking fish, has what special ability?

a. It can fly as well as walk.

b. It can regenerate a lost limb.

c. It builds dams.

7

The golden poison frog is only 3.5 cm long, but it can carry enough poison to kill how many people?

a. 2

b. 5

c. 10

8

What do amphibians use to take oxygen into their bodies?

a. Gills

b. Lungs

c. Their skin

9

Amphibians ruled the world for 100 million years.

True or false?

10

The goliath frog is the world's largest frog. How big can it get?

a. 32 cm long, weighing 3.25 kg

b. 22 cm long, weighing 2.25 kg

c. 12 cm long, weighing 1.25 kg

AMPHIBIANS

1

c.
'Amphibian' is a Greek word – 'amphi' means 'both' and 'bio' means 'life'. When put together, this literally translates to 'both kinds of life', suggesting that amphibians live in two different stages and two different environments – first as tadpoles in water and then as adult creatures on land.

2

True.
Some species of amphibian are vegetarian when they are tadpoles, but they will be eating other creatures by the time they are adults.

3

a.
Some salamanders can weigh 50 kg and reach 180 cm in length.

5

c.
Spanish ribbed newts have sharp ribs that can puncture through their sides and secrete poison. They use this as a defence mechanism against predators.

4

True.
It's a handy way to tell frogs and toads apart. Frogs also have a narrower body than toads and their toes on their back feet are webbed.

6

b.
The axolotl can regenerate almost any body part, including limbs, its tail, and even parts of its brain.

7

c.
Golden poison frogs have enough poison to kill 10 grown humans.

8

a, b and c.
Amphibians use gills when they are tadpoles and lungs as adults, with some species also drawing in oxygen through their skin.

9

True.
Around 350 million years ago, amphibians were the rulers of the land animals on Earth. About 250 million years ago reptiles began to take over, including dinosaurs.

10

a.
The goliath frog is a monster of an amphibian, measuring 32 cm long and weighing in at 3.25 kg!

EVOLUTION

1 When did the first animals appear on Earth?
a. 500,000 years ago   b. 15 million years ago   c. More than 650 million years ago

 2 The book *On the Origin of Species* kick-started the idea of evolution. Who wrote it?
a. Charles Darwin   b. Albert Einstein   c. Stephen Hawking

 3 The animals on which islands inspired Darwin's ideas?
a. The Shetland islands   b. The Galapagos islands   c. The Isle of Wight

 4 We learn a lot about the evolution of animals from fossils, but what are fossils?
a. Pictures of ancient animals drawn by cave dwellers.
b. The remains or marks of plants and animals preserved in rock.
c. Computer models of what scientists think ancient animals looked like.

 5 What type of animal did birds evolve from?
a. Amphibians   b. Mammals   c. Dinosaurs

 6 Humans and apes share a common ancestor, but which creatures are our closest living relative?
a. Gorillas   b. Chimpanzees   c. Baboons

 7 When did our modern human species, *Homo sapiens*, first appear?
a. Around the same time as birds evolved – 145 million years ago
b. When the dinosaurs went extinct – 65 million years ago
c. Around 120,000 years ago

 8 Which of these creatures is the closest relation to a blue whale?
a. Great white shark   b. Whale shark   c. Hippopotamus

 9 Which of these events can shape the evolution of new species?
a. Small changes in the surrounding environment
b. Genetic mutations in individual animals
c. Cataclysmic events such as an asteroid striking the earth

10 What colour were all human eyes 10,000 years ago?
a. Brown   b. Blue   c. Green

1 **c.** Scientists have found fossils of animals that are 558 million years old and have worked out that animals must have been around for a long time before that.

2 **a.** Darwin dropped out of his university medical studies and followed his passion for natural history.

3 **b.** Darwin sailed aboard a ship called HMS Beagle.

4 **b.** The oldest fossils are nearly 3.5 billion years old.

5 **c.** Birds are the only living dinosaurs. Their nearest living relatives are members of the crocodile family.

6 **b.** Humans share 99% of their DNA with chimpanzees.

7 **c.** Around 120,000 years ago – humans have walked this planet for a relatively short amount of time.

8 **c.** Sharks are fish and are not close relations of the whale, which is a mammal. But hippos and whales share a common ancestor that lived 50 million years ago. Whales are closer relatives to animals like cows and pigs than they are to sharks.

9 **a, b and c.** Many factors can influence how species evolve. The animals that are most suited to a particular environment will be more likely to reproduce.

10 **a.** All human eyes were brown 10,000 years ago. Blue eyes only evolved 6000–10,000 years ago. All people with blue eyes today inherit them from a single common ancestor.

MOLLUSCS AND CRUSTACEANS

TRUE or **FALSE**

1

African giant snails can grow to over 30 cm long.

2

Lobsters have eight legs.

3

Many slugs and snails are both male and female at the same time.

DID YOU KNOW?

Molluscs are the largest marine group, and make up over 20% of all marine species.

4

Colossal squid and giant squid have the largest eyes of any animal.

5

Mantis shrimps punch their prey to death.

6

The largest crab in the world lives in the forests of Japan.

7

All crabs walk sideways.

8

Lobsters have blue blood.

9

A geoduck is a type of clam that can live to be over 100 years old.

10

Oysters create pearls to attract a mate.

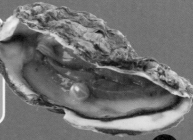

MOLLUSCS AND CRUSTACEANS

1

TRUE.
The largest-ever African giant snail measured 39.3 cm from nose to tail and weighed 900 g.

2

FALSE.
Including their front pincers, lobsters have 10 legs.

3

TRUE.
Most land slugs and snails are 'hermaphrodites' and increase their chances of passing on their genes by being male and female.

4

TRUE.
Squid eyes may be as large as 28 cm in diameter.

5

TRUE.
Mantis shrimps have two fist-like appendages that they bash crabs and clams with at over 50 mph. They hit with a force of over 1500 newtons – if we were that strong for our size we could punch through steel!

6

FALSE.
The Japanese spider crab lives at the bottom of the sea. And a good thing too; the largest ever found measured 3.7 m from claw to claw.

7

FALSE.
Most species of crab do walk sideways because the joints in their legs flex in that direction. However, there are a few species that can walk forwards and backwards.

8

TRUE.
Lobsters have a protein in their blood that contains copper, making their blood blue.

9

TRUE.
The geoduck usually lives to be around 140 years old and the oldest ever found was 168.

10

FALSE.
An oyster makes a pearl when a piece of grit or a parasite gets caught in its body. It covers the irritant in layers of shiny nacre which over several years creates a pearl.

FREAKY FISH

1

What is this unusual-looking fish called?

a. Banjofish
b. Drumfish
c. Guitarfish

2

The largest fish in the world is...

a. The great white shark
b. The whale shark
c. The sunfish

3

Anglerfish catch their prey by hypnotising them with a song.

True or false?

4

Electric eels stun their prey with an electric shock that is how strong?

a. Up to 860 volts
b. Up to 520 volts
c. Up to 240 volts

5

The Antarctic blackfin icefish has what colour blood?

a. Black
b. Blue
c. Transparent

6

What makes the coelacanth such a special fish?

a. It can turn its body inside out.
b. It swims backwards.
c. It was thought to be extinct.

7

Flying fish use specially evolved fins to leap out of the water to escape predators. What is the longest time a flying fish is known to have glided for?

a. 45 seconds
b. 25 seconds
c. 5 seconds

8

What type of creature is a seahorse?

a. A fish
b. A shrimp
c. A tiny water horse

9

How does the frogfish move around the water?

a. It 'walks' along the seafloor on its special fins.

b. It hitches a ride on a shark.

c. It swims upside down.

10

Why is the male jawfish so unusual?

a. It has two heads.

b. It incubates its young in its mouth.

c. It keeps stones in its mouth to spit at predators.

DID YOU KNOW?

The Spanish name for jawfish is 'bocas grandes', which literally means 'big mouths'!

FREAKY FISH

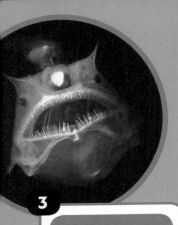

1

c.
Guitarfish look like a cross between sharks and rays, with a long body, flattened head and broad 'wings'.

2

b.
The whale shark can reach 18 m long and may weigh around 30 tonnes.

3

False.
Anglerfish have a lure dangling from their forehead. Shrimp think the lure is a tasty snack and swim right up to the waiting mouth.

4

a.
Electric eels can stun their prey with up to 860 volts.

5

c.
The Antarctic blackfin icefish, which survives icy sea temperatures, has transparent blood. It also has no scales, and its bones are so thin that you can see its brain!

DID YOU KNOW?
Anglerfish can grow up to 1 m in length, and swim as deep as 3000 m under the ocean's surface.

6

c.
Scientists thought the coelacanth had been extinct for millions of years, until one was caught in 1938. There are now two species known to exist.

7

a.
With the help of updrafts from waves, flying fish can cover 400 m in a glide.

8

a.
Seahorses may not look like fish, but they are related to sticklebacks.

9

a.
Frogfish have wide fins which they use to help them 'walk' across the seabed when looking for food to eat.

10

b.
Jawfish are 'mouthbrooders' – they protect their young from predators by keeping them in their mouth for the first 8–10 days of their lives.

DESERT ANIMALS

DID YOU KNOW?

A gemsbok's horns can reach around 120 cm in length. They use them to defend their territory and themselves if a predator gets too close.

1
The largest hot desert in the world is in Australia.

2
The fennec fox from Arabia has the largest ears for its size of any carnivore.

3
Sidewinder snakes move sideways to sneak up on prey.

4
The gemsbok antelope from the Namib desert doesn't need to drink water to survive.

5
The dromedary camel stores water in its hump to use later.

6
The shovel-nosed lizard uses its unusual nose to flip beetles over onto their backs.

7
The golden mole finds its food by hiding in the sand and sensing the vibrations of creatures on the surface nearby.

8
The spotted sandgrouse carries water to its chicks in its beak.

9
Camels have long eyelashes to help attract a mate.

10
Sand cats live in burrows in the ground.

DESERT ANIMALS

TRUE or **FALSE**

1

FALSE.
The largest hot desert is the Sahara, in Africa. With an area of 9.2 million km², it is around the same size as the US.

2

TRUE.
The fennec fox's huge ears help to radiate heat away.

3

FALSE.
Sidewinding helps the sidewinder snake minimise body contact with the hot desert sand.

4

TRUE.
The gemsbok antelope can get all the moisture it needs from its food.

5

FALSE.
The dromedary's hump is a store of fat. However, the dromedary can drink a third of its own bodyweight in water in just 10 minutes.

6

FALSE.
The shovel-nosed lizard uses its nose to help it 'swim' through loose sand.

7

TRUE.
The golden mole is completely blind.

8

FALSE.
The spotted sandgrouse soaks its belly feathers with water and takes it to the chicks that way.

9

FALSE.
Camels' long eyelashes help keep sand out of their eyes.

10

TRUE.
Sand cats shelter from the day's heat in their underground dens and hunt at night.

1 Polar bears enjoy snacking on penguins.
True or false?

2 Is it colder in the Arctic or the Antarctic?
a. Arctic   b. Antarctic   c. Both the same

3 What colour is polar bears' skin?
a. White   b. Pink   c. Black

4 Orcas are actually a species of dolphin.
True or false?

5 Which of these animals changes colour in the winter?
a. Arctic fox   b. Ptarmigan   c. Snowshoe hare

6 What is this Arctic-dwelling creature (right)?
a. Elephant seal   b. Narwhal   c. Unicorn

7 Walruses use their tusks to dig holes in the ice.
True or false?

8 Emperor penguins stop their eggs from freezing by...
a. Blowing on them
b. Keeping them on top of their feet
c. Wrapping them in seal fur

9 Seals, penguins and whales all have a special layer of fat to keep themselves warm. What is it called?
a. Blubber   b. Flubber   c. Rubber

10 How long can elephant seals hold their breath underwater for?
a. 20 minutes   b. 40 minutes   c. 100 minutes

1 **False.** Polar bears live in the Arctic and penguins in the Antarctic, so they never meet in the wild.

2 **b.** In winter, the North Pole averages around –40°C, but the South Pole averages –60°C, so the Antarctic is much chillier!

3 **c.** Polar bears' hair is also transparent – it only looks white because of the way it scatters light.

4 **True.** Orcas are actually the largest members of the dolphin family. They are highly intelligent and social animals.

5 **All of them!** They all change their brown or black summer coats for a white winter wardrobe to blend in with the snow.

6 **b.** The narwhal's 'tusk' is actually a canine tooth.

7 **True.** Walrus tusks are very strong and can reach 1 m long. They also use them for fighting and pulling themselves up onto the ice.

8 **b.** Emperor penguins stop their eggs from freezing by keeping them on top of their feet in a brood pouch.

9 **a.** This layer of fat known as blubber covers their entire bodies, except for their fins, flippers and flukes.

10 **c.** Elephant seals have even dived as deep as 2388 m under the surface in search of a tasty squid.

77

MOUNTAIN MASTERS

1
What is the world's only species of high-mountain cattle?
a. Yak
b. Gnu
c. Aberdeen Angus

2
The world's largest bird of prey lives in the Andes mountains of South America. What is it called?
a. Condor
b. Gondor
c. Mouton

DID YOU KNOW?
Snow leopards are often known as 'ghosts of the mountain' because they are almost never seen.

3
The vicuña is a South American member of the camel family. How does it cope with breathing the thin mountain air?
a. It has two sets of lungs.
b. It can hold its breath for an hour.
c. It has a high number of red blood cells.

4
The Tibetan stone loach is Asia's highest-altitude fish. At what height can it live?
a. 3200 m
b. 4200 m
c. 5200 m

5
What is another name for the snow leopard?
a. Ounce
b. Pounce
c. Bounce

6

How do pikas ensure they have enough food throughout the year?

a. They steal food from snow leopards.
b. They make hay and store it.
c. They migrate down the mountain to grasslands in the winter.

7

Marmots live in many mountainous areas of the world. What type of creature is a marmot?

a. Rabbit
b. Cat
c. Squirrel

8

Why does the lammergeier (also known as the bearded vulture) drop bones from great heights?

a. To knock out its prey
b. To shatter them in order to get to the bone marrow inside
c. To attract a mate

9

Can you identify this animal that lives in the Andes mountains?

a. Giant panda
b. Spectacled bear
c. Kodiak bear

10

Mountain goats can climb rock faces steeper than 60° in pitch. What helps them do this?

a. Sharp dewclaws that stop them from slipping
b. Cloven hooves that can spread apart
c. Pads on their feet that grip the rock

MOUNTAIN MASTERS

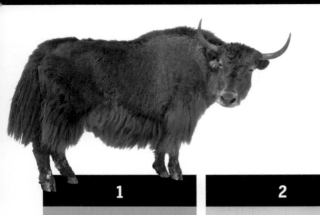

1

a.
The yak is native to the Himalayas.

2

a.
The Andean condor's wingspan can reach 3 m.

3

c.
Red blood cells carry oxygen through the body, and the vicuña has 14 million red cells per mm^3 of blood, compared with 5 million red cells per mm^3 blood in humans at low altitudes.

4

c.
5200 m

5

a.
The name 'ounce' is thought to be linked to its Latin name, Panthera uncia.

6

b.
Pikas harvest grasses and other vegetation and store them as piles of hay in sheltered places.

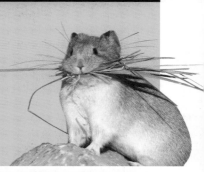

7

c.
Marmots are the largest member of the squirrel family.

8

b.
Lammergeiers are true masters of the mountain. They find bones from dead animals and then drop them from a great height in order to crack them open and get to the nutritious marrow inside.

9

b.
The spectacled bear is the only bear native to South America. Can you guess how it got its name?!

10

a, b and c.
Mountain goats also have powerful neck and shoulder muscles to help them climb steep slopes.

FOREST CREATURES

1

What is a squirrel's nest called?
a. Den
b. Drey
c. Domain

2

The pine marten lives in forests in Scotland, Wales and parts of England. What kind of creature is it?
a. Mustelid
b. Rodent
c. Bird

3

Which forest is home to the greatest number of species on Earth?
a. Redwood forest
b. Tropical rain forest
c. Nottingham forest

4

Which panda lives in the mountain forests of the Himalayas?
a. Giant panda
b. Red panda
c. Black panda

5

Many animals that live in forests have prehensile tails. What does prehensile mean?
a. The tail can wave to signify danger.
b. The tail can regenerate if it is chopped off.
c. The tail can grip branches.

6

Jaguars are big cats that live in the rain forests of South America. Their name comes from a local word 'yaguar' which means...

a. Fierce beast
b. Cat of many spots
c. Big-toothed tree cat

7

Which of these rodents lives in the trees?

a. Bank vole
b. Common shrew
c. Common dormouse

8

This animal is the closest living relative of the giraffe and it lives in the dense tropical Ituri Forest of Central Africa. What is its name?

a. Kakapo
b. Okapi
c. Pikachu

9

Flying squirrels don't fly like birds, but glide from tree to tree using parachute-like areas of skin.
True or false?

10

Sloths live in the trees of South America and are famous for moving slowly. How long can it take them to digest a single meal?

a. A day
b. A week
c. A month

FOREST CREATURES

1

b.
A squirrel's nest is known as a drey.

2

a.
The mustelid family includes weasels, badgers and otters – as well as the pine marten.

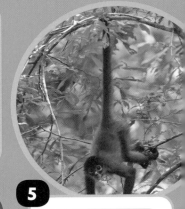

3

b.
Rain forests may contain as much as 75% of all living species.

4

b.
The red panda lives in the Himalayas, and is an endangered animal.

5

c.
A prehensile tail acts as a fifth limb and is very useful.

6

a.
Jaguars are expert hunters who will eat almost any creature they can find.

7

c.
The dormouse hardly ever comes down from the trees while it is active during the summer, building its own nests in the branches or sleeping in empty birds' nests.

8

b.
The okapi is also known as the forest giraffe.

9

True.
Many types of creatures, including marsupial sugar gliders and flying squirrels, have developed this ability to glide.

10

c.
Sloths' metabolisms are so slow that it takes them a long time to digest their food.

ENDANGERED ANIMALS

1 The Arabian oryx was saved from extinction by a special breeding programme in captivity.

True or false?

2 Why are Alpine musk deer targeted by poachers?

a. Musk is a strong scent that can be used in cosmetic products.

b. The deer have pure white coats.

c. Their antlers have medicinal properties.

3 How many tigers are left in the wild today?

a. 3900

b. 32,000

c. 320,000

4 What activities are causing sea turtle numbers to go down?

a. They are being hunted for their meat.

b. Chemicals dumped in the ocean destroy their habitats.

c. Fishermen catch them accidentally.

5 There are only around 60 Javan rhinoceroses left on the planet.

True or false?

6

Stag beetles are a protected species in the UK. What environment is crucial to their survival?

a. Open moorland

b. Perfectly clean running water

c. Dead and decaying wood

7

Grey parrots are now a 'vulnerable' species. What is one big reason for their decline?

a. Their habitats are being burned.

b. They are very good talkers so people want them as pets.

c. They have contracted a human-made virus.

8

The Masai giraffe population has fallen by around 50% in the last 3 decades.
True or false?

9

Tasmanian devils are found in Australia as well as the island state of Tasmania.
True or false?

10

Scientists think that the Bramble Cay melomys, a small Australian rodent, is on the verge of extinction.
True or false?

ENDANGERED ANIMALS

1

True.

The Arabian oryx was then reintroduced to the wild.

2

a.

There are artificial alternatives to musk, but some deer are still poached.

3

a.

Sadly there are only 3900 tigers in the wild today as some people still hunt tigers, to use their body parts in medicine, for their skins or even just for sport.

4

a, b and c.

Sea turtles are being endangered in a variety of ways by human activity.

5

True.

Javan rhinoceroses were once the most widespread of Asian rhinoceroses but now they are dangerously close to extinction.

6

c.

Stag beetles lay their eggs in rotting wood. So rather than clearing all fallen trees from parks and gardens, it can help the beetles to leave some old trunks and branches behind.

9

False.

Tasmanian devils were once common in Australia, however, now they can only be found in Tasmania.

7

b.

Many grey parrots are sold illegally at high prices to be pets.

10

False.

The Bramble Cay melomys went extinct in 2016 and scientists believe that it is the first extinction of a mammal species due to human-caused global warming.

8

True.

Unfortunately, numbers of this species of giraffe are in decline because of poaching and expanding human populations.

AT THE BEACH

1 **What creature is this on the right?**
a. Sea cucumber
b. Sea anemone
c. Sea onion

2 **Which rock pool creature is also a type of explosive mine?**
a. Crab
b. Whelk
c. Limpet

3 **What makes a hermit crab unusual?**
a. It lives in a rock pool with no other creatures in it.
b. It lives in the shell of another creature.
c. It lives above the high tide line.

4 **Rock pools are refreshed by the incoming tide. But what causes the tides?**
a. The Moon
b. Magic
c. The Sun

5 **How many eggs can a common starfish produce?**
a. 25,000   b. 250,000   c. 2.5 million

6 Seaweed, such as bladderwrack and kelp, is what type of organism?
a. Algae
b. Plant
c. Fungus

7 What type of seabird is this on the right?
a. Oystercatcher
b. Puffin
c. Guillemot

8 The largest jellyfish in British waters is known as the dustbin-lid jellyfish. True or false?

9 What type of creature is a cuttlefish?
a. Cephalopod
b. Fish
c. Mammal

10 Sometimes on rocky coasts you might see spraints. What are spraints?
a. Flying fish that have crashed onto land
b. Discarded crab shells
c. Otter dung

1 **b.** Sea anemone.

2 **c.** Limpet mines cling to the side of their target.

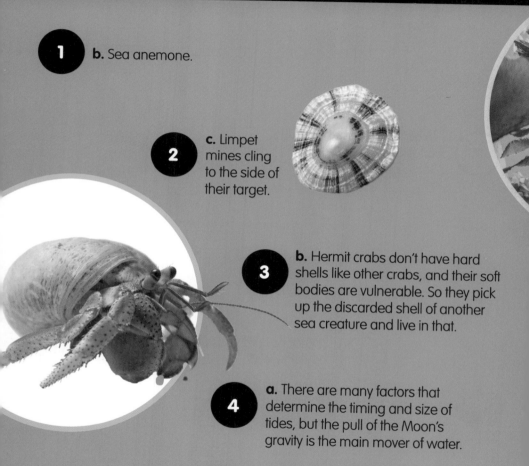

3 **b.** Hermit crabs don't have hard shells like other crabs, and their soft bodies are vulnerable. So they pick up the discarded shell of another sea creature and live in that.

4 **a.** There are many factors that determine the timing and size of tides, but the pull of the Moon's gravity is the main mover of water.

5 **c.** A common starfish can produce 2.5 million eggs.

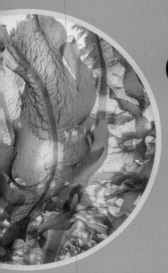

6   **a.** Seaweed is a type of algae and has many uses, including as food, in medicine and as a fertiliser.

7   **b.** Puffins are nicknamed 'Sea Parrot' or sometimes 'Clown of the Sea'.

8   **True.** The dustbin-lid jellyfish is also known as the barrel jellyfish and can grow to around 90 cm in diameter.

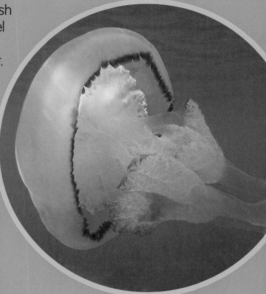

9   **a.** Cuttlefish are in the same biological class as squid and octopuses.

10   **c.** Spraints – also known as otter dung – are a tell-tale sign that otters live nearby, and they have an aroma all of their own!

HAPPY TRAVELLERS

1
The longest mammal migrations are made by caribou.

2
Monarch butterflies sometimes travel across the Atlantic Ocean by mistake.

3
Animals migrate to escape predators.

4
Some animals never stop migrating.

5
The biggest migration in terms of animal numbers takes place every dawn and dusk.

6
The Arctic tern migrates from the Arctic all the way to the Antarctic and back again every single year.

7
After a common swift first takes to the air, it will never touch land again in its life.

8
Atlantic salmon are born in rivers, migrate to the sea to live most of their life, then return to exactly the same river they were born in to breed and die.

10
Reindeer in Norway start their migration on exactly the same day each year.

9
Wildebeest migrate in a giant loop, following the rains.

HAPPY TRAVELLERS

QUIZ 23 ANSWERS

1

FALSE.
Grey whales make the longest mammal migrations, swimming from the Arctic Ocean to the coast of Mexico to breed.

2

TRUE.
Monarch butterflies leave Canada to fly 3000 km south to Mexico for the winter, and sometimes get blown off course.

3

FALSE.
Migration lets animals find food when it is most available, and helps them avoid climate conditions that would harm them.

4

TRUE.
'Nomadic' creatures have no fixed home and spend the year always moving from place to place.

5

TRUE.
When the Sun sets, billions upon billions of tiny sea creatures migrate from deep underwater to the surface of the sea to eat algae and plankton. When the Sun rises, they go back to the depths.

6

TRUE.
The Arctic tern flies more than 35,000 km every year and spends more time in daylight than any other creature.

7

FALSE.
Common swifts do land to breed. However, they do spend up to two years constantly on the wing, travelling over 500,000 km on one epic journey.

10

FALSE.
Reindeer migration in Norway happens sometime around late April or early May but no one knows what makes the reindeer decide when to start. One day they just head off!

9

TRUE.
Around 1.2 million wildebeest (also called gnus) make the loop-shaped migration every year.

8

TRUE.
Atlantic salmon smell their way back to their birth place.

97

The four examples in each question are types of which animal?

1 **Chinstrap · Rockhopper · King · Emperor**
a. Crab   b. Salmon   c. Penguin

2 **House · Wood · Field · Deer**
a. Mouse   b. Rat   c. Pig

3 **Horseshoe · Long-eared · Pipistrelle · Vampire**
a. Crab   b. Cat   c. Bat

4 **Cane · Fire-bellied · Midwife · Natterjack**
a. Toad   b. Frog   c. Bat

5 **Sea · Golden · Crowned · Harpy**
a. Vulture   b. Eagle   c. Cat

6 **Passenger · Band-tailed · Wood · Nicobar**
a. Sparrow   b. Swift   c. Pigeon

7 **Blue · Bull · Tiger · Greenland**
a. Shark   b. Salmon   c. Penguin

8 **Fishing · Marbled · African golden · Jungle**
a. Heron   b. Dog   c. Cat

9 **King · Tiger · Freshwater · Indian**
a. Cobra   b. Eel   c. Prawn

10 **Desert · Four-toed · Amur · Hugh's**
a. Rat   b. Hedgehog   c. Sloth

1 **c.** Penguin

2 **a.** Mouse

3 **c.** Bat

4 **a.** Toad

5 **b.** Eagle

6 **c.** Pigeon

7 **a.** Shark

8 **c.** Cat

9 **c.** Prawn

10 **b.** Hedgehog

INSECTS

1

How many species of insect have been identified so far?

a. 100,000
b. 500,000
c. 1 million

2

Roughly how many nectar-collecting trips does it take bees to make 1kg of honey?

a. 100,000
b. 50,000
c. 1000

3

Which of these types of life evolved first?

a. Dinosaurs
b. Insects
c. Flowering plants

4

Silk is made by the silkworm, which is actually the larva form of a type of insect. Which type?

a. A beetle
b. A moth
c. A wasp

5

Glow-worms (see above) are actually beetles.

True or false?

6

The largest-ever locust swarm may have contained around 12.5 trillion individual creatures and occurred in Africa.

True or false?

7

The fastest insect is the Australian tiger beetle. It can run 171 body lengths in a second. If humans could do the same, they would run at 1077 km/h.

True or false?

8

The largest flying insect ever was a dragonfly with a wingspan of 70 cm.

True or false?

9

What insect larvae did Napoleon's doctors use to clean soldiers' wounds?

a. Maggots
b. Caterpillars
c. Grubs

10

Mayflies are known for their...

a. Very short wings
b. Very short lives
c. Very short legs

INSECTS

1

c.
1 million types of insect have been identified so far but there could be as many as 10 million species of insect!

2

a.
100,000 trips – that's why we say bees are busy...

3

b.
Insects evolved more than 400 million years ago.

4

b.
The silkworm is the caterpillar form of the moth, and it creates the silk to make its cocoon.

5

True.
Glow-worms are indeed beetles.

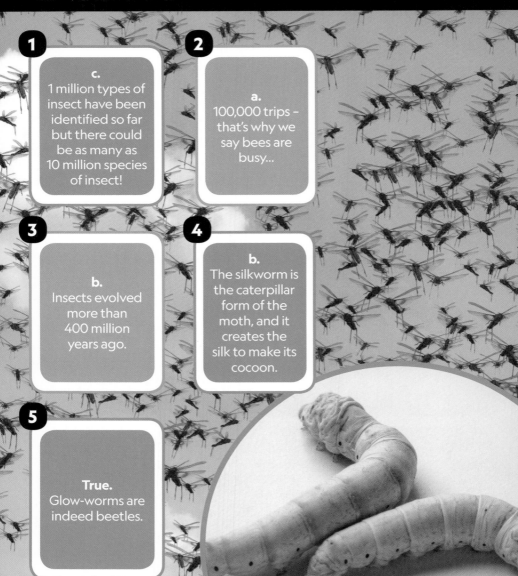

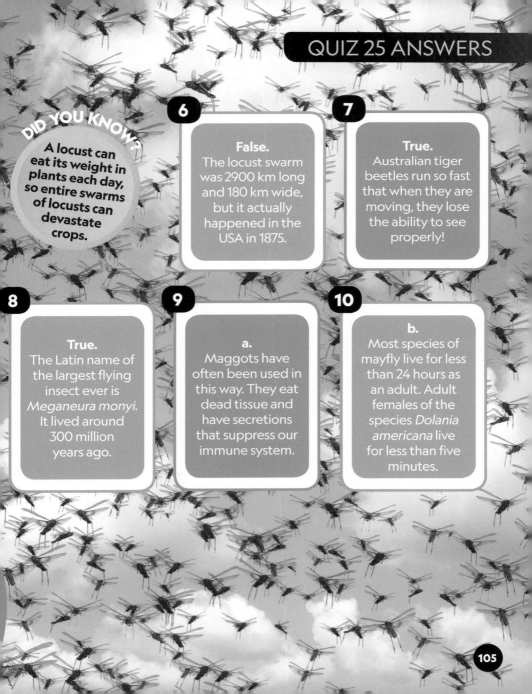

DID YOU KNOW?

A locust can eat its weight in plants each day, so entire swarms of locusts can devastate crops.

6

False.
The locust swarm was 2900 km long and 180 km wide, but it actually happened in the USA in 1875.

7

True.
Australian tiger beetles run so fast that when they are moving, they lose the ability to see properly!

8

True.
The Latin name of the largest flying insect ever is *Meganeura monyi.* It lived around 300 million years ago.

9

a.
Maggots have often been used in this way. They eat dead tissue and have secretions that suppress our immune system.

10

b.
Most species of mayfly live for less than 24 hours as an adult. Adult females of the species *Dolania americana* live for less than five minutes.

Many groups of animals have their own special name.
See if you can match each group name to the animals it describes.

1	A bloat	...of lions
2	A clutter	...of owls
3	A prickle	...of porcupines
4	A convocation	...of caterpillars
5	A romp	...of dolphins
6	A wisdom	....of wombats
7	An ambush	...of camels
8	A train	...of crows
9	A sloth	...of monkeys
10	A mischief	...of mice
11	A troop	...of bears
12	A pod	...of tigers
13	An army	...of otters
14	A parliament	...of eagles
15	A murder	...of hippos
16	A pride	...of spiders

COLLECTIVE NAMES

QUIZ 26 ANSWERS

1. A bloat of hippos
2. A clutter of spiders
3. A prickle of porcupines
4. A convocation of eagles
5. A romp of otters
6. A wisdom of wombats
7. An ambush of tigers
8. A train of camels
9. A sloth of bears
10. A mischief of mice
11. A troop of monkeys
12. A pod of dolphins
13. An army of caterpillars
14. A parliament of owls
15. A murder of crows
16. A pride of lions

ANIMALS IN MYTHS AND STORIES

1

A centaur is a legendary animal made up of which creatures?

a. An eagle and a lion
b. A man and a horse
c. A horse and an eagle

2

Which animals deliver mail in the *Harry Potter* books?

a. Owls
b. Cheetahs
c. Snails

3

Animals feature in many Bible stories. Which creature tempted Eve to eat the apple in the Garden of Eden?

a. A lion
b. A serpent
c. A wombat

4

In the common folktale, how did Androcles make friends with a lion?

a. He brought it food when it was hungry.
b. He pulled a thorn from its paw.
c. He saved one of its cubs from a river.

5

According to legend, which saint slew a dragon?

a. Saint Patrick
b. Saint Johnstone
c. Saint George

6

Which white animal did Alice follow to get to Wonderland?

a. Rabbit

b. Polar bear

c. Beluga whale

7

In the film *Finding Nemo*, what type of fish is Nemo?

a. Sunfish

b. Mudfish

c. Clownfish

8

What breed of dog is Scooby Doo?

a. Yorkshire terrier

b. Labrador

c. Great Dane

9

Animals are very important in the Hindu religion. The god Hanuman is represented by which creature?

a. Eagle

b. Elephant

c. Monkey

10

Which animated film is about a lion, a hippo, a zebra and a giraffe that escape from New York zoo?

a. *Matilda*

b. *Madagascar*

c. *Martinique*

ANIMALS IN MYTHS AND STORIES

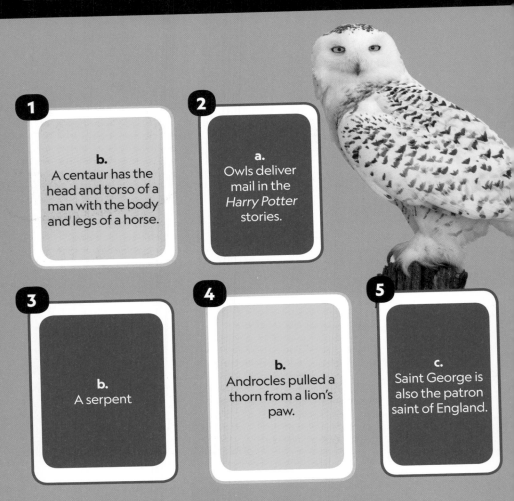

1

b.
A centaur has the head and torso of a man with the body and legs of a horse.

2

a.
Owls deliver mail in the *Harry Potter* stories.

3

b.
A serpent

4

b.
Androcles pulled a thorn from a lion's paw.

5

c.
Saint George is also the patron saint of England.

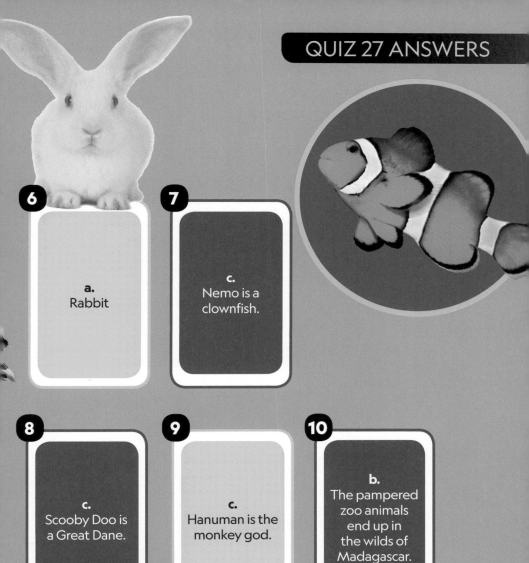

6

a.
Rabbit

7

c.
Nemo is a clownfish.

8

c.
Scooby Doo is a Great Dane.

9

c.
Hanuman is the monkey god.

10

b.
The pampered zoo animals end up in the wilds of Madagascar.

BEAUTIFUL BIRDS

1 Which bird lays the largest egg relative to its size?

a. Ostrich   b. Eagle   c. Kiwi

2 Bowerbirds get their name from the impressively decorated bowers – or nest-like structures – that male bowerbirds make in order to attract a mate.

True or false?

3 'Swan upping' is an 800-year-old tradition of counting the swans that live on which English river?

a. The Tyne   b. The Nile   c. The Thames

4 Birds often use rising columns of warm air to lift them higher. What are these columns of air called?

a. Thermals
b. Cyclones
c. Air-cases

5 Owls can rotate their heads through 360°.
True or false?

6 Most of the world's birds are passerines – what does passerines mean?

a. Birds that sing
b. Birds of prey
c. Perching birds

 7 Hunting with birds of prey, such as falcons, is still practised today. When did this activity first start?

a. Around 2000 BC
b. During the Roman Empire
c. In the Middle Ages

 8 What is the world's smallest bird?

a. Dwarf sparrow
b. Bee hummingbird
c. Lesser spotted wren

 9 Ostriches may not be able to fly, but they are good runners. How fast can they run?

a. 70 km/h
b. 50 km/h
c. 30 km/h

 10 Birds of prey have amazing eyesight. How much keener is a hawk's eyesight than a human's?

a. Twice as good
b. Four times as good
c. Eight times as good

BEAUTIFUL BIRDS

1 **c.** A kiwi can lay two eggs in two days, each of which weighs 26% of its bodyweight.

2 **True.** Bowerbirds go the extra mile to attract a female... Satin bowerbirds, for example, decorate their bowers with blue shiny objects!

3 **c.** Swan upping is carried out on the River Thames. It used to be a way of determining who owned the swans (and who could therefore eat them), but now it is done to count the cygnets and check on the swans' health.

4 **a.** Coasting up on a thermal uses much less energy than flapping your wings.

5 **False.** But some owls can turn their heads 270 degrees in either direction.

6 **c.** Passerines (perching birds) include thrushes, larks, crows, starlings and finches.

7 **a.** Falconry is a very ancient practice and started around 2000 BC.

8 **b.** The bee hummingbird lives in Cuba and is only 6 cm long.

9 **a.** Ostriches' long legs can stretch 5 m in one stride.

10 **b.** Hawks can spot a rabbit much further away than a human would be able to.

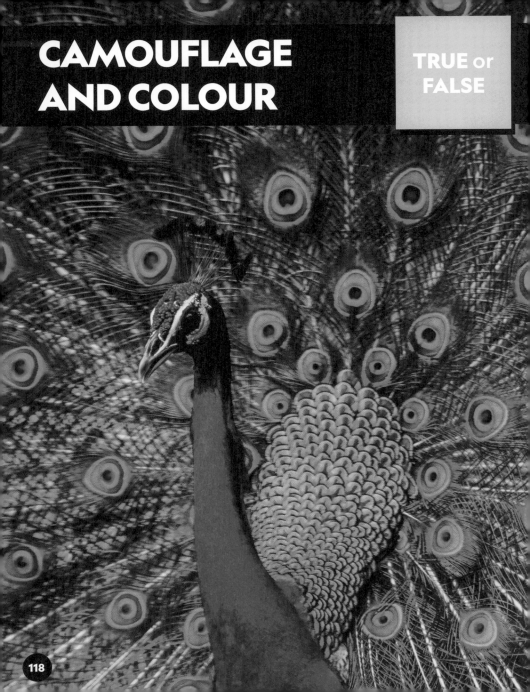

CAMOUFLAGE AND COLOUR

TRUE or FALSE

1
Some animals copy the colours and patterns of a more harmful animal to scare predators.

2
The polar bear is white to make it difficult for grizzly bears to hunt it.

3
The tawny frogmouth lives safely in trees by camouflaging itself as a broken branch.

4
Most chameleons can change their skin colour.

5
The decorator crab got its name because of the way it adds shells to its burrow.

6
Peacocks use their huge tail feathers to help them blend in with dense foliage.

7
The leafy sea dragon not only looks like seaweed, it sways in the water exactly as seaweed does.

8
A squid can hide itself from predators by squirting out a cloud of ink.

9
Glass frogs got their name because their bodies are transparent, making them very difficult to see in the dim jungle.

10
Many butterflies have 'eyespots' on their wings – markings that can make the butterfly look like the head of a predator.

CAMOUFLAGE AND COLOUR

1

TRUE.
This is called Batesian mimicry. For example, some harmless hoverflies have evolved to look like wasps.

2

FALSE.
Polar bears' white appearance makes it easier for them to sneak up on their prey without being seen.

3

TRUE.
The tawny frogmouth is hardly ever seen.

4

TRUE.
Chameleons change their skin colour as camouflage and to communicate with other chameleons.

5

FALSE.
The decorator crab decorates itself, covering its back with seaweed, sponges and stones that act as camouflage.

6

FALSE.
Peacocks' splendid feathers are a way of showing off to attract a mate.

7

TRUE.
The leafy sea dragon's swaying makes its camouflage even more effective!

8

TRUE.
Almost all squid and octopus species can squirt ink.

9

TRUE.
Many other animals, including jellyfish, use transparency as a way to hide.

10

TRUE.
Some moths and other insects also have eyespots.

1

How does the Egyptian vulture use tools?

a. It uses a stick to knock fruit to the ground.

b. It digs canals to gather fish.

c. It throws stones to break ostrich eggs.

2

Beavers fell trees to build dams — how big was the largest-ever beaver dam?

a. 85 m long

b. 850 m long

c. 8500 m long

3

The largest-ever bird's nest was 2.9 m wide, 6 m deep and weighed more than two tonnes. Which type of bird built it?

a. Bald eagle

b. Ostrich

c. Albatross

4

What human machine do crows in Japan use to crack walnuts?

a. Drill

b. Car

c. Lawnmower

5

What food do chimps use a long twig to collect?

a. Honey

b. Sunflower seeds

c. Ants

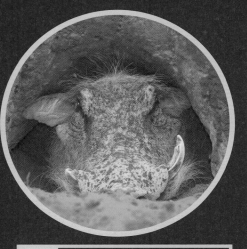

What African pig uses a burrow?

6

a. Warthog

b. Giant forest hog

c. Mukota

Which animal home is a popular dish in China?

7

a. Beaver lodge

b. Bee hive

c. Bird's nest

A wasp's nest is also known as...

8

a. An aviary

b. A vespiary

c. An apiary

What is so unusual about the nests that sociable weaver birds build?

9

a. They are made entirely of feathers.

b. They build huge communal nests with individual family 'apartments'.

c. They are made in tunnels underground.

In northeast Brazil, there is a collection of over 200 million termite mounds, with some of the mounds being 4000 years old. How big an area do these mounds cover?

10

a. An area the size of London

b. An area the size of Wales

c. An area the size of Great Britain

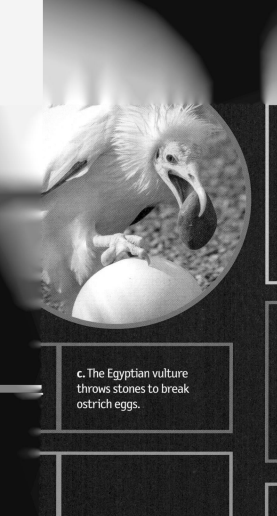

3 **a.** The largest-ever bird's nest was built by a pair of bald eagles in Florida, USA.

c. The Egyptian vulture throws stones to break ostrich eggs.

4 **b.** Crows in Japan have been spotted putting walnuts in front of the tyres of cars stopped at red lights. When the cars drive away, the nuts are cracked.

2 **b.** Beavers have been building the dam in Alberta, Canada, for more than 40 years.

5 **c.** Chimps dip sticks in ant hills to get the ants from inside.

a. Warthogs shelter in their burrow at night.

b. Sociable weaver birds also use different nesting materials for different purposes, like using big sticks for the roof and sharp and spiky pieces of straw at the entrance to deter any predators.

9

c. Bird's nest soup has been popular for over a thousand years. It is made from the nests of cave swiftlets, which are constructed from the birds' saliva.

c. The termite mounds are around 2.5 m tall and 9 m across and are so extensive that they can be seen by satellite.

10

b. A vespiary is the name for a wasp's nest.

TIE BREAKER

If there's a draw between two players,
try this tie breaker question...
closest answer wins!

HOW MANY TIMES A SECOND DOES A BEE BEAT ITS WINGS?

TIE BREAKER

A bee can beat its wings 190 times every second!
(That works out at a whopping 11,400 times
a minute, or 684,000 times an hour!)

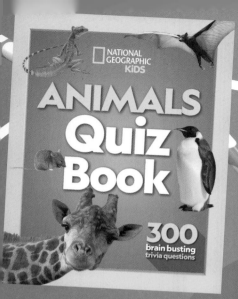

NATIONAL GEOGRAPHIC KiDS
ANIMALS Quiz Book
300 brain busting trivia questions

NATIONAL GEOGRAPHIC KiDS
OUR WORLD Quiz Book
300 brain bustin trivia question

NATIONAL GEOGRAPHIC KiDS
Quiz books

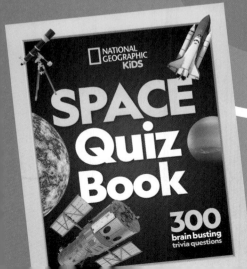

NATIONAL GEOGRAPHIC KiDS
SPACE Quiz Book
300 brain busting trivia questions

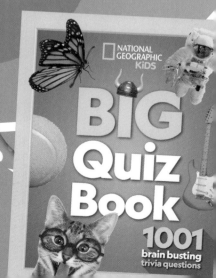

NATIONAL GEOGRAPHIC KiDS
BIG Quiz Book
1001 brain busting trivia questions